**SYMPHONIC THEMES FOR FLUTE**

# Symphonic Themes

Wise Publications
London/New York/Paris/Sydney/Copenhagen/Madrid

**Exclusive Distributors:**
Music Sales Limited
8/9 Frith Street,
London W1V 5TZ, England.
Music Sales Pty Limited
120 Rothschild Avenue,
Rosebery, NSW 2018, Australia.

Music Sales Corporation
257 Park Avenue South,
New York, NY10010, United States of America.

This book © Copyright 1994 by
Wise Publications
Order No. AM91913
ISBN 0-7119-4029-0

Music processed by Interactive Sciences Limited, Gloucester
Designed by Hutton & Partners

Music Sales' complete catalogue describes thousands of titles and is available in full colour sections by subject, direct from
Music Sales Limited. Please state your areas of interest and send a cheque/postal order for £1.50 for postage to:
Music Sales Limited, Newmarket Road, Bury St. Edmunds, Suffolk IP33 3YB.

# CONTENTS

# Symphony No.2 in D
## 3rd Movement Theme

Composed by Ludwig van Beethoven (1770–1827)

# Symphony No.6 (Pastoral)
## 3rd Movement Theme

Composed by Ludwig van Beethoven (1770–1827)

# Symphony No.3 in E♭ (Eroica)
## 1st Movement Theme

Composed by Ludwig van Beethoven (1770–1827)

**Bright**

# Symphony No.1 in C Minor
## 4th Movement Theme

Composed by Johannes Brahms (1833–1897)

# Symphony No.3 in F
## 3rd Movement Theme

Composed by Johannes Brahms (1833–1897)

# Symphony No.9 in E Minor
## (From The New World)
### 2nd Movement Theme

Composed by Antonin Dvořák (1841–1904)

# Symphony No.8 in G
## 3rd Movement Theme

Composed by Antonin Dvořák (1841–1904)

# Symphony No.9 in E Minor
## (From The New World)
### Finale

Composed by Antonin Dvořák (1841–1904)

# Symphony No.88 in G
## Largo

Composed by Franz Joseph Haydn (1732–1809)

# Symphony No.94 in G (Surprise)
## 2nd Movement Theme

Composed by Franz Joseph Haydn (1732–1809)

# Symphony No.97 in C
## 2nd Movement Theme

Composed by Franz Joseph Haydn (1732–1809)

# Symphony No.104 in D (London)
## 2nd Movement Theme

Composed by Franz Joseph Haydn (1732–1809)

# Symphony No.3 (Scottish)
## 3rd Movement Theme

Composed by Felix Mendelssohn (1809–1847)

**Moderately slow**

# Symphony No.4 (Italian)
## 2nd Movement Theme

Composed by Felix Mendelssohn (1809–1847)

# Symphony No.4 (Italian)
## 3rd Movement Theme

Composed by Felix Mendelssohn (1809–1847)

# Symphony No.6 in F
## Minuet And Trio

Composed by Wolfgang Amadeus Mozart (1756–1791)

# Symphony No.50 in D
## 2nd Movement Theme

Composed by Wolfgang Amadeus Mozart (1756–1791)

# Symphony No.4 in C Minor
## Andante

Composed by Franz Schubert (1797–1828)

# Symphony No.5 in B♭
## 2nd Movement Theme

Composed by Franz Schubert (1797–1828)

**Moderately**

# Symphony No.8 in B Minor (Unfinished)
## 1st Movement Theme

Composed by Franz Schubert (1797–1828)

# Symphony No.5
## Extract from Andante Cantabile

Composed by Piotr Ilyich Tchaikovsky (1840–1893)

**Slowly and with feeling**

# Symphony No.6 (Pathétique)
## March Theme

Composed by Piotr Ilyich Tchaikovsky (1840–1893)

# Symphony No.6 (Pathétique)
## 1st Movement Theme

Composed by Piotr Ilyich Tchaikovsky (1840–1893)

# Symphony No.6 (Pathétique)
## 2nd Movement Theme

Composed by Piotr Ilyich Tchaikovsky (1840–1893)